Grade 5

Treasures

INDIANA

ISTEP+ Format Assessment

- Unit
- Benchmark

Mc Graw Hill **Macmillan McGraw-Hill**

Contents

Answer Keys

Indiana Academic Standards

Writing Rubrics

Anchor Papers

Reteaching and Intervention Charts

Introduction to the Unit Assessment

The Unit Assessment is designed to measure your students' mastery of specific skills. The test questions use formats students will encounter on the Indiana Statewide Testing for Educational Progress Plus (ISTEP+) in Grade 6. The Unit Assessment includes questions that cover the following areas:

Reading Comprehension: Strategies and Skills
Listening Comprehension
Vocabulary Strategies
Grammar, Mechanics, and Usage
Text Features and Study Skills
Literary Elements
Writing

When scheduling the assessments, you will need to decide whether to administer them in one or more sessions. You may choose to give the Unit Assessment in one sitting or schedule the writing for another time.

How to Use the Unit Assessment

The Unit Assessment includes fiction and nonfiction passages and questions focusing on the main skills taught throughout the unit. There is also a writing prompt that requires the same type of writing as the one focused on in the unit. Included on **pages 306–307** are writing rubrics to help you score the writing. To help students become more comfortable with timed writing tests, you may want to give students 40–55 minutes to address the writing prompt.

At the back of this book you will find anchor papers for five different types of writing. The student writing samples provide illustrations of the kinds of responses students are likely to write, as well as the most common kinds of errors found in students' writing at this grade level. The samples are written responses to the writing prompts used in the Unit Assessment.

Each Unit Assessment includes multiple-choice and constructed-response questions in the same style and format as the ISTEP+. Students should fill in their answers directly in the test booklet.

Each question is correlated to an Indiana Academic Standard. The correlations follow the Student Evaluation Chart for each test. Each standard has been given a code for correlation. The coded standards are listed on **pages 292–303** of this book for easy reference.

Using the Results to Inform Instruction

Use the results of the Unit Assessment as a formative assessment tool to help monitor student progress. Information gathered by evaluating the results of this assessment can also be used to diagnose specific strengths and weaknesses of your students. If scores from the Unit Assessment are used to help determine report card grades, then you can consider them to be summative assessments.

The scores from the Unit Assessment should be one of multiple measures used to help make instructional decisions for the coming unit. Analyze which skills students have mastered and which ones require reteaching. This information, along with the results of other assessments and your own observations, can be used to determine grouping and instructional decisions. Another way to use the results of the Unit Assessment is to compare it with the results of the Weekly Assessments. Determine if changes in instruction or additional small-group support improved students' scores.

The **Reteaching and Intervention Charts** on **pages 330–335** will help you develop teaching plans.

Administering the Unit Assessment

Each Unit Assessment consists of multiple-choice and constructed-response questions. The format of the test parallels that of the ISTEP+. You may want to explain each section of the test to students the first time you administer it.

- For the multiple-choice questions, students should fill in the circle next to the best answer. Remind students to fill in the circle completely for each answer.
- For the constructed-response questions, students should write their answers in the space provided on the page.

The **Answer Key** to score the tests can be found on **pages 281–286.**

Directions: Say: *Write your name and the date on the cover of your test booklet.* When all students are done, say: *Open the booklet to page 2.*

General Procedures

Before the test: Distribute copies of the Unit Assessment.

During the test: Monitor students' test-taking behavior to make sure that each student is following the directions and writing responses in the correct places. Answer questions about procedures and materials, but do not help them answer the test questions.

After the test: Before collecting the papers, make sure that students have written their names on the cover of the test booklet.

© Macmillan/McGraw-Hill

Scoring Instructions

Using the Student Evaluation Charts

After each Unit Assessment there is a Student Evaluation Chart. It lists all of the skills covered and the number of the question that assesses each skill.

- In the column labeled "Number Correct," fill in the point value for the number of questions answered correctly for each skill. Count the total point value of correct responses, and write the number for each subtest above the total possible score.

- Add the scores for each skill (point value for the number of items answered correctly) to determine the total test score.

- To convert these raw test scores to percentages, divide the point value for the number answered correctly by the total number of possible points. Example: A student gets 9 out of 12 possible points; 9 divided by 12 = .75, or 75%.

Multiple-choice questions are worth one point each, and short-response questions are worth two points each. Extended-response questions are worth ten points each, as they are scored both on reading comprehension and writing skills. The writing prompt is worth ten points as well. Rubrics to help you score the extended-response questions and the writing prompt are included on **pages 305–307.**

Evaluating the Scores

The primary focus of the Unit Assessment is to measure student progress toward mastery of each skill. Scores that fall below the 80th percentile suggest that students require additional instruction before mastery of that skill can be achieved.

Evaluating the results of this assessment provides specific information about students' daily instructional needs. We recommend that you use these results for instructional planning and reteaching opportunities. Compare these results with your own observations of students' work and identify objectives that still need reinforcement. Incorporate these into your instructional plans for the coming unit for individual, small-group, or whole-group instruction as indicated.

Grade 5, Unit 1

This Unit Assessment is designed to measure your students' mastery of the skills taught in the unit. The test assesses all of the following areas:

- Listening Comprehension
- Vocabulary Strategies
- Reading Comprehension
- Text Features and Study Skills
- Grammar, Mechanics, and Usage
- Literary Elements
- Writing

Listening Comprehension, pp. 2–3

The questions in the Listening Comprehension section address comprehension skills and strategies, as well as vocabulary strategies taught in this unit. Say: *Listen while I read this story to you. You will be asked to answer four questions based on this story. Listen carefully. We will begin now.*

An Unusual Day

Carol opened her eyes and stretched her arms. She felt as though she had slept a long, long time.

She remembered that she'd been dressing some mannequins in a department store window. Suddenly, she had become drowsy.

She looked down at what she was wearing. It was not an outfit that she could remember: suede jacket, jeans, and soft boots. Where had they come from? "I must have slept longer than I thought," Carol said to herself. She turned to leave the store window, but suddenly her arms and legs stiffened. She couldn't move.

Outside the window, three women were approaching the store, pointing at her boots. Then a father and two little girls were staring at her jacket. But they all moved away. As they left, Carol tried desperately to attract their attention—to say that she was one of them—but not a sound or motion could she make.

When dusk came and the streets emptied, Carol found that she could move again. As the lights went on, she noticed the handsome mannequin in a purple ski outfit standing beside her. Could she be mistaken or had he winked at her? It seemed too much to hope for that one of the other models in the display might be alive, too. She turned and smiled at him.

Now have students turn to page 2 and say: *Numbers 1 through 4 are based on the story you just heard, "An Unusual Day." The first three questions are multiple choice. Read all four answer choices for each question. Then fill in the circle next to the best answer. The fourth question is constructed-response. Write your answer to this question in the space provided on the page. When you have finished, put down your pencils and look at me. You may begin now.*

Vocabulary Strategies; Reading Comprehension; Text Features and Study Skills; Grammar, Mechanics, and Usage; Literary Elements, pp. 4–18

This part of the test assesses vocabulary strategies and reading comprehension strategies and skills, and the text features and study skills learned throughout the unit. It also assesses grammar, mechanics, and usage, as well as literary elements.

Have students turn to page 4. Say: *You will now answer some multiple-choice and constructed-response items. Some questions will be based on a passage or graphic. Some questions will not have a passage or graphic. Read each question carefully. For each multiple-choice question, read all four of the answer choices. Then fill in the circle next to the best answer. For each constructed-response item, write your answer in the space provided on the page. When you get to the bottom of page 18, put down your pencils and look at me. You may begin now.*

Have students answer questions 5–30 and stop on page 18.

Writing Prompt, p. 19

This part of the test assesses the unit writing mode.

Have students turn to page 19 and say: *Read the instructions next to the writing icon. Then turn to page 20 and read the writing prompt carefully. Be sure that you **completely** respond to all parts of the writing prompt. Use pages 21 and 22 for pre-writing and planning. Then write your essay starting on page 23. Check your writing using the Editing Checklist on page 26.*

Make sure students understand what they are expected to do

Say: *When you have finished writing, put down your pencils and look at me. You may begin writing now.*

Name _____

Date _____

ISTEP+ Format Unit Assessment

TESTED SKILLS AND STRATEGIES

- **Listening Comprehension**
- **Vocabulary Strategies**
- **Reading Comprehension**
- **Text Features and Study Skills**
- **Grammar, Mechanics, and Usage**
- **Literary Elements**
- **Writing**

 **Macmillan McGraw-Hill**

Name _____

Numbers 1 through 4 are based on "An Unusual Day."

1 **What made Carol think she had slept for a long time?**

   Ⓐ She was still very tired.

   Ⓑ She couldn't move her legs.

   Ⓒ It was getting late.

   Ⓓ Her clothes were unfamiliar.

2 **Why did Carol smile at the mannequin?**

   Ⓐ He looked funny.

   Ⓑ He was her friend.

   Ⓒ They shared a joke.

   Ⓓ She hoped he was alive.

Go On

3 Read this sentence from the story.

Suddenly she had become drowsy.

Which word is a synonym for *drowsy*?

Ⓐ awake

Ⓑ sleepy

Ⓒ dressy

Ⓓ afraid

4 What TWO things happened to Carol that made her realize that she was a mannequin?

1) _____

_____

2) _____

_____

The Ice Palace

As I eagerly approached my secret ice palace in the park, I remembered my last visit. The ice-covered branches had made tinkly crystal wind chimes in the breeze. The diamond-crusted pond had reflected thousands of rainbows on the powdery drifts which lay around it. I had lain down in the snow, looking up at the branches above. It was so cold that day that I could see my breath, but I had felt all warm and cozy, hugged by the snow. The afternoon sun shone brightly, which caused the ice on the trees to melt. Little drops had fallen around me, splashing on my face. It had almost seemed as though the trees were crying.

Today it wasn't cold at all. The sun glowed happily in the sky, causing rivers to run through the shrinking piles of snow on the ground. When I finally reached the pond, my crystal wonderland was gone! Nothing was there but a shrunken muddy hole surrounded by sorry black skeletons. The ice palace had been destroyed by the same nature that had created it.

Go On →

Name _____

Numbers 5 through 7 are based on "The Ice Palace,"
found on page 4.

5 **Read this sentence from the story.**

*The diamond-crusted pond had reflected thousands of
rainbows on the powdery drifts which lay around it.*

Which of the following words is a *compound* word?

Ⓐ thousands

Ⓑ rainbows

Ⓒ powdery

Ⓓ diamond-crusted

6 **What is the tone of this story?**

Ⓐ angry

Ⓑ amazed

Ⓒ matter-of-fact

Ⓓ playful

7 **Using details from the story, describe TWO clues in the
first paragraph that suggest what will happen at the end.**

1) _____

_____

2) _____

_____

Go On →

Name _____

Sailing the Seas

Put together wood and canvas, power them with wind and tide, and you have the only means of ocean travel used for hundreds of years—the sailing ships. In them, the early explorers gained knowledge of other peoples and other lands. When all the world had been charted, trade between countries became very important.

To answer the need for increased trade, the American "clipper ship" was designed. With three tall masts and many square-rigged white sails, clipper ships were among the most beautiful sailing vessels ever built. These important ships sailed the world's seas from 1845 to the 1860s.

Clipper ships were not designed as works of art; they were planned for trade. Cargoes of goods produced on the East Coast needed to be shipped from New York and Boston to the gold miners in California, to traders in China, and to the colonists in Australia. For these purposes, clipper ships had to be fast and have great cargo space.

The finest designer and builder of clipper ships was Donald McKay, an immigrant to the United States from Nova Scotia. Between the launching of his ship, the *New World,* in 1845 and the closing of his boatworks in 1873, McKay built some of the largest and fastest sailing ships ever known. He designed everything to work well, and he used the most modern tools of his day. Derricks lifted the huge masts into place. Power saws cut timbers. The selected wood was then finished by lathes, machines that hold and spin pieces of wood while cutting tools shape them.

However, the same inventiveness that gave McKay more modern tools also led to the invention of steamships. Because steamships did not have to rely on wind and tide, they could be larger and more reliable than any clipper ship. The desire to get there first with the most cargo caused traders to turn to steam. The age of the sailing ship had ended.

© Macmillan/McGraw-Hill

Go On

Name _____

Numbers 8 through 13 are based on "Sailing the Seas," found on page 6.

8 **Read this sentence from the passage.**

Clipper ships were not designed as works of art; they were planned for trade.

Which word in the sentence helps you understand the meaning of *designed*?

Ⓐ works

Ⓑ art

Ⓒ planned

Ⓓ trade

9 **Read this sentence from the passage.**

Because steamships did not have to rely on wind and tide, they could be larger and more reliable than any clipper ship.

What of these is a *compound* word?

Ⓐ steamships

Ⓑ larger

Ⓒ reliable

Ⓓ clipper

10 **Read this sentence from the passage.**

However, the same inventiveness that gave McKay more modern tools also led to the invention of steamships.

Which word is a synonym for *inventiveness*?

Ⓐ clumsiness

Ⓑ gracefulness

Ⓒ creativeness

Ⓓ laziness

Go On

11 **Which of the following BEST summarizes the passage?**

Ⓐ The only means of ocean travel for hundreds of years were sailing ships.

Ⓑ Clipper ships carried goods from the East Coast to places as far as China and Australia.

Ⓒ The finest designer and builder of clipper ships was Donald McKay.

Ⓓ Clipper ships were the most important ships on the sea until the age of the steamships.

12 **Use the Venn diagram to show ONE similarity and ONE difference between the clipper ships and the steamships.**

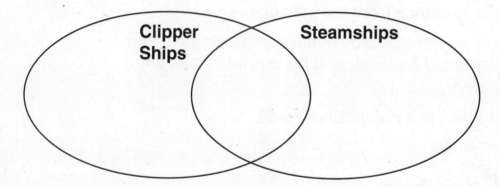

13 **Explain TWO reasons why traders thought steamships were better than clipper ships.**

1) _____

_____

2) _____

_____

© Macmillan/McGraw-Hill

Go On